This book belongs to............

Dedicated to the children of lockdown for their courage and resilience during difficult times.

First published in the UK in 2021 by Rebecca Tonks Publishing.

Second Edition

This edition is published by Rebecca Tonks Publishing in 2021.

ISBN: 978-1-8384803-0-1

A CIP catalogue record for this book is available from the British Library.

Further information about this book can be found on

Instagram @bec_tonks_illustrator
&
www.facebook.com/BecTonksIllustrator

Icky Sticky!!

Rebecca Tonks

Oh Icky Sticky,

we must not hug!

Please wash your hands

and

beware of the

bug.

Stay safe,

keep apart

and try to be clean.

Smile at a distance,

with space in between.

Naughty

Icky Sticky

will try to move quick

but we know the rules and won't fall for its trick.

Be safe and **stay home,**

away from harm.

Be **happy** and **chill**

and try to **stay calm.**

5 o'clock every day

we put the TV on.

A messy haired man tells us what needs to be done.

He says

"We must stay away

from school...

learning from home

will be the new rule."

Monday to Friday
for a while will change.

Mom and Dad as teachers

may seem a bit strange.

If you feel it's too much

and

your brain will explode...

Take a breath,

count to ten...

and calmly **reload.**

Make time to **exercise**

and be **outside.**

We must **socially distance,**

but we don't have to hide.

Icky Sticky...

We might not see you, but we know where you are,

driving all around in your **invisible car.**

Hiding amongst the **fruit and veg** at the shop.

Then
moving
through
aisles
with a

skip and a hop!

The adults are told to put **face masks** on and

to **anti-bac** their hands so germs will be gone!

NOW...

We'll **help** each other and

from our driveway we'll shout...

"Do you need any **groceries**, when we're out and about?"

We can lift each other's spirits and bring a **smile.**

With regular video calls, we'll connect for a while.

It may feel scary, like nothing's the same

but **always** look for...

the **rainbow** beyond the rain.

For what this little bug does not see,

is that a **warrior potion** will set us all

free!

Our doctors and nurses have been working their **magic.** So the end for **Icky Sticky** will surely be tragic!

This **magic potion** will be **free** for us all. It will spread across the land in an **ordered** call.

Those that are shielding and need it to last,
will be given their protective armour...

super-fast.

Our **heroes,** the NHS, will then make sure...
that to everyone else,
they'll deliver some more.

It'll be truly **wonderful** when this moment comes!

A time to wrap our arms round our **best chums!!**

This nasty bug is getting smaller I'm sure.

Soon the fear of **Icky Sticky** will be ...

NO more!

So…

Be calm and remember

Icky Sticky won't last.

If we all follow the **rules**

it'll be a thing of the

past!

Brighter times will soon be here.........

Everyone will
wave and cheer.

Printed in Great Britain
by Amazon